❖   ❖   ❖

Listening to Your Soul

❖   ❖   ❖

DICK WILSON

❖ ❖ ❖

Listening to Your Soul

❖ ❖ ❖

The Way to Harmony, Health & Happiness

Index compiled by Lyn Greenwood

SAFFRON WALDEN
THE C.W. DANIEL COMPANY LIMITED

First published in Great Britain in 1999
by The C.W. Daniel Company Limited
1 Church Path, Saffron Walden,
Essex, CB10 1JP, United Kingdom

ISBN 0 85207 328 3

Produced in association with Book Production Consultants, plc,
25–27 High Street, Chesterton, Cambridge, CB4 1ND
Typeset by Cambridge Photosetting Services, Cambridge
Printed and bound by St Edmundsbury Press,
Bury St Edmunds, Suffolk

❖ ❖ ❖

Dedication

❖ ❖ ❖

To my Grandchildren, the new Generation,
with love and blessings.

Contents

Acknowledgements

I would like to express my deep-felt appreciation to Anthea Courtenay for all her assistance and encouragement during the writing of this book. I am truly grateful to Anthea for helping me to express and explain some very complicated and deep concepts so that, hopefully, those who are interested in this field can better understand the spiritual dimension involved in Health and Healing.

I would also like to acknowledge with gratitude the support I have received from Dennis Milner whose own two books contributed to my better understanding of this complex field.

Finally my thanks to everyone, particularly my family, who encouraged me to write this book.

❖　❖　❖

The Soul

❖　❖　❖

The Soul can be defined as our spiritual body: it has its roots in eternity. It carries the records of all our thoughts, activities and experiences acquired over many incarnations. These memories and records permeate every cell of the Physical Body, so that each of us is a reflection of the present state of our Soul on its long journey to spiritual perfection. The Soul is also aware of the experiences we need and choose to deal with in each lifetime and imbues our every cell with the mission to be accomplished in our current life. If we are not fulfilling our mission and have lost sight of our life plan, then we experience a persistent state of unease at a very deep level, caused by the conflict between our self and our Soul. Thus the lack of harmony between our spiritual purpose and the life we lead is one of the main causes of chronic illness today.

Introduction

Over many years it has been my good fortune to be involved with both homoeopathic medicines and hands-on healing, and I have seen their positive effects over and over again. Yet I have never come across a satisfactory explanation of how they work, or of the real causes and cure of illness. This has puzzled and concerned me, particularly as it has become my vocation to promote both these safe and effective therapies, and I feel I should be able to explain what I am promoting.

In particular, I have been baffled by the many diverse and sometimes strange techniques employed by healers, on the whole successfully. In this field no-one, so far as I know, has yet provided an explanation that satisfactorily defines the principles which would apply to all these techniques.

I have always felt that there must be one principle underlying this whole field, but for a long time this eluded me. However, over the last few years, partly as a result of my close involvement with the manufacture and distribution of homoeopathic medicines and the Bach Flower Remedies, together with some profound and enlightening experiences in the field of healing, and partly from the many books I have read on this wide and complex subject, I have finally discerned a possible explanation. It is this explanation that I offer to readers, perhaps new to this field, not as the definitive answer but as one possibility, and as a basis for further exploration.

In all, there have been three strands to my thinking, which – together with my work with homoeopathy and the Bach Flower Remedies – have come together to provide this explanation. One is the work of Max Freedom Long, whose researches earlier this century in Hawaii – then the most geographically isolated part of Polynesia – resulted in books on the Huna philosophy of the ancient Polynesians. Discovering his book *The Secret Science Behind Miracles* was a defining moment for me. In it he describes the Huna beliefs and traditions, and in particular provides an understanding of some of the causes and successful treatment of illness.

I read Max Freedom Long's book with growing interest, for the ancient philosophy he describes seems to offer a convincing explanation not only of why people fall ill, but how they can be permanently cured of their illnesses, including the mental and emotional problems for which psychotherapy might be called on today. I went on to read all Long's books, as well as most of the others that have been written on the Huna tradition.

In this booklet I shall be describing, briefly and simply, the main tenets of the Huna tradition and how they can be applied to dealing with illness. I would urge readers who want more in-depth information on this fascinating subject to read the books by Max Freedom Long and others listed in the Bibliography.

The second strand of my thinking is my personal experience of etheric healing, to which I was introduced by my uncle, Andrew Wilson. In the 1960s he founded Thornhill Healing Centre, just outside Glasgow, which he ran successfully until the mid-1980s. He was not a healer himself, but had been interested in healing all his life, and had the motivation, commitment and resources to create a wonderful healing sanctuary.

I became involved with Thornhill during the 1970s and used to assist at healing sessions. These included the widespread method of laying on of hands, and also a more dramatic form of healing: the healer-medium, Albert Best, while under the direction of his spirit guides, would remove tumours, for example, from the patient's body.

Impressive as this type of healing can appear, what really interested me was the fact that although everyone experienced some or total relief of physical and emotional pain, not everybody was healed in the sense of being completely cured. It was amazing that some people could be reprieved even of terminal cancer, while others were not. This led me to wonder why – what was the missing factor? Many of the answers to this question were supplied by the Huna philosophy, and also communicated through the teachings of the spirit doctors who spoke through Albert Best.

The third strand of my thinking is based on beliefs that I have personally held for many years which in turn were derived from the teaching of the Austrian mystic, philosopher and educationalist Rudolf Steiner, and two important books by Dr Dennis Milner, a scientific researcher at Birmingham University.

In the 1970s Dr Milner produced two remarkable books, *The Loom of Creation*, co-written with Edward Smart, and *Explorations of Consciousness* (both unfortunately out of print). My uncle Andrew Wilson and his charitable foundation helped to finance the research for these books, which are serious studies by technological scientists into fields usually ignored by science – including para-psychology, mysticism and expanded awareness, mediumship, the human aura or energy field, and psychic surgery.

The Loom of Creation offers a model of the wider meaning of man's existence and true being, one which supplies the answers to many questions including the very purpose of our existence. *Explorations of Consciousness* describes the experiences of a group of research scientists and technologists who explored the expansion of their inner consciousness through trance techniques.

In the first two chapters of this booklet I have distilled, in a simplified form, much of the philosophy emerging from these two books and from Steiner's thinking, in order to provide a basic structure for the further theories outlined here.

Dick Wilson
October 1998

❖ ❖ ❖

1. What is a
Human Being?

❖ ❖ ❖

It may be useful at the outset to explain some of the terminology used in this book, so that the reader can start with a clear picture. Different schools of thought may have different meanings and names for some of the terms. This does not make any of them 'wrong', and readers should not let this confuse them. The aim here is to express somewhat complex ideas as clearly as possible.

All esoteric and spiritual philosophies recognise that the human being consists of much more than the Physical Body. The world religions all acknowledge the existence of an eternal, undying Soul, depicted in different ways according to different cultures. At the same time, the ancient spiritual philosophies of the East describe systems of invisible energy surrounding and flowing through the body, which provide a link between our physical and spiritual selves. The role of these energies in our health is becoming widely accepted today in the field of complementary medicine and healing.

Chinese medicine, for example, is based on the existence of meridians, channels of energy running through the body; our physical health and emotional wellbeing depend on the harmonious flow of energy (*Qi*, pronounced 'chi') through these meridians. Indian yoga and medicine relate to a system of chakras, seven energy centres aligned down the body from the crown of the head to the base of the spine, which take in and give out energy (prana). Health and emotional harmony depend on the free, unblocked flow of energy within and between the chakras. Both these systems are becoming increasingly accepted in the western world, while in western spiritual thought we are hearing more and more about the existence of a Higher Self, the highest part of us, which is our link with our spiritual source.

How do all these elements fit together? The model I have found most helpful, and which is followed here, is based on the thinking of Steiner and Milner. According to this model, the human being consists of five main aspects: the Physical, Etheric and Astral Bodies, the Ego – which we know as our individual identity – and the Higher Self. The Soul [see p.12] encompasses three of these.

The Physical Body

The human body is the physical vehicle for the evolution of the Spirit. It is the result of aeons of evolution, which began when spiritual beings decided to incarnate on earth in order to experience the challenges of life within a material environment.

Human beings are therefore spiritual beings. Our ultimate purpose is to evolve sufficiently to return permanently to the spiritual realm from which we came, by developing our spirituality while in physical form. This process takes many lifetimes, in between which we return temporarily to our spiritual home to absorb and learn from our earthly experiences.

The body is surrounded by an energy field, invisible to most people but capable of being felt and sometimes seen by those whose sensitivities are developed. This energy field can be divided into two main parts, the Etheric Body and the Astral Body.

The Etheric Body

The Etheric Body is an energy body that closely surrounds the Physical Body and permeates every part of it. It is responsible for the body's form and functioning, maintaining its physical, nervous and chemical systems. It is a blueprint of every cell, tissue and fluid in the Physical Body.

The Etheric Body controls every action we perform, and all our involuntary bodily processes –

everything in fact but the voluntary muscles. It registers and stores as memory all our experiences, actions and thoughts throughout life.

The Etheric Body maintains our life processes at all times, including periods of sleep and unconsciousness. When it is separated from the body we are no longer alive. At death, its memory of our life experiences is absorbed and retained by the Soul.

The Astral Body*

The Astral Body is a key component of the spiritual make-up of the human being. It is the architect of the Etheric Body, which it surrounds like a multi-coloured, egg-shaped radiation of light. Steiner refers to it as our Soul-body, or the sentient part of the Soul. It is through the Astral Body that we experience sensations, thoughts, emotions, desires and reactions. It is the energy body responsible for our thinking, our voluntary actions and, importantly, through it we exercise our free will. When we wish to perform an action, we activate the Astral Body by thinking, and the thought process works through the Etheric Body in order for the Physical Body to act appropriately.

The Astral Body's natural environment is the spiritual world, and each night during sleep it returns to this realm. There it is balanced and restored to

*Some esoteric systems divide the Astral Body into a number of sub-divisions, but for the sake of simplicity these will not be expanded on here.

harmony, returning when we re-awaken to activity. During this time the bodily processes are kept going by the Etheric Body.

Without the active presence of the Astral Body within us, we remain unconscious, or in deep sleep.

The Ego

The Ego, our individual identity, is the active presence within the three bodies – the Physical, Etheric, and Astral. It is our eternal self. It is the original divine droplet, the God that dwells in all of us. Steiner compares the Ego to a drop of water taken from the ocean, which has the same composition as the ocean, but cannot claim to be the ocean. As the drop is to the ocean, so is our Ego to the Divine. Human beings can always find the Divine within themselves because it is from the Divine that their essential being springs.

Many human beings, however, are unaware of their own divine nature, and the Ego's task on earth is to develop the spiritual potential of its being, while temporarily cut off from its spiritual origins. This separation came about when human beings were first created: the Higher Selves of humanity could not incarnate fully into physical bodies without the risk of losing touch with their spiritual origins. It was therefore decided that only a part of the spiritual entity should be incarnated, in the form of the Ego: the part that remains in the spiritual realm is the Higher Self, the divine part of our Soul-being.

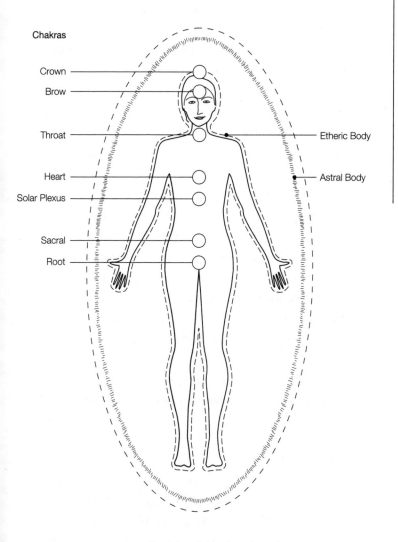

Chakras

Crown

Brow

Throat ———————————————— Etheric Body

Heart ———————————————— Astral Body

Solar Plexus

Sacral

Root

The Human Energy System
The Seven Main Chakras,
the Etheric and Astral Bodies

The Higher Self

The Higher Self is our connection with divinity, it is the perfect part of the Soul which has never left the Godhead. Our main contact with it occurs during deep sleep and in meditation.

Connected with the Divine, it is constantly working to draw the rest of our Soul-being to an understanding of its own true essence and nature. When the rest of our Soul-being eventually comes to this perception, and has evolved to be of like kind and essence as the divine part of our Soul, our spiritual purpose will finally be fulfilled.

Thus there is the potential, through the guidance of the Higher Self, for the Ego to be in attunement with the whole. And no matter how far we go astray, there still remains within each one of us the pattern of and link to perfection through which we may regain full attunement with the whole.

The individual Higher Self is exclusive to human beings. Plants and animals possess group Higher Selves, and do not have individual Egos.

The Soul

The Soul can be defined as our spiritual body: it has its roots in eternity. It is said that God created man in His image: more accurately, the Soul was originally created in the image of God. It carries the records of all our thoughts, activities and experiences acquired over many incarnations. These memories and records permeate every cell of the

Physical Body, so that our Ego is a reflection of the current state of our Soul. The Soul is also aware of the experiences we need to deal with in each lifetime, and imbues our every cell with the mission to be accomplished in our current life.

Although we refer to it as a unity, the Soul has three main components, the Ego, the Astral Body, and the Higher Self. While living in a physical incarnation, the Ego is separated from the divine part of its Soul-being, the Higher Self. At death, however, the two are consciously re-united.

What is a Human Being?

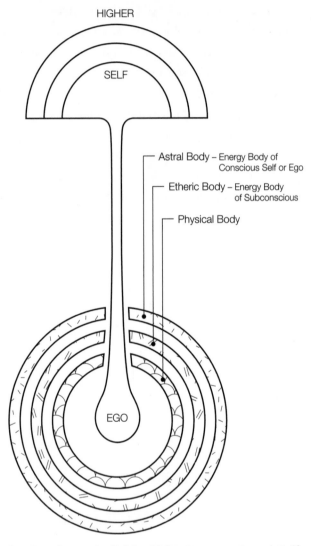

HIGHER

SELF

Astral Body – Energy Body of
Conscious Self or Ego

Etheric Body – Energy Body
of Subconscious

Physical Body

EGO

The Ego is our individual identity, our eternal Self.
It is the active presence within the three bodies –
the Physical, Etheric and Astral. It remains
connected to the Higher Self during our
physical incarnation.

2. The Purpose of Creation

Anyone who follows a spiritual path senses that life is more than a haphazard series of events: there is a meaning to existence, and an over-all purpose to the creation of the universe and humanity. For me, this has also been described most convincingly in the ideas of Steiner and Milner.

According to Steiner, human beings form only part of an evolutionary stream of spiritual beings, at the centre of which is the Godhead – not a personal God, and certainly not the judgmental God of the Old Testament, but a state of whole-ness, the source of all consciousness from which everything in creation emanates. The Godhead is surrounded by a hierarchy of spiritual beings, all of whom are working towards the spiritual evolution of humanity, and of which our Souls are a part.

The evolution of humanity began when the Spiritual Hierarchy close to the Godhead decided to further the evolution of all Spirit beings by creating a world of matter. In the Spirit realm, they were unable fully to appreciate their own perfection, since they had nothing to contrast it with. *The only way they could experience their own spirituality, and appreciate the state of pure love in which they existed, would be to experience the opposite of this perfect state.* They could do this by undergoing life in a physical form in a material world, which would provide Spirit beings with experiences and challenges not available to them in the realm of pure spirit. To achieve this, it was necessary to create a material environment together with a physical vehicle, the human body, into which a Spirit being could incarnate.

In order to form the world of matter, the Spiritual Hierarchy contributed part of its Spirit body to make up the various forms of life. In the material world, therefore, all matter is ultimately formed of spiritual beings or entities at various levels of consciousness, fashioned by formative forces following the archetypal patterns of the Spiritual Hierarchy.

The Beginning of Creation: The Mineral Kingdom

From the beginning, creation has been controlled by two important life forces, one spiralling downwards and inwards, the other radiating upwards and outwards. On Earth, the one manifests as gravity, the other as the Sun. These two forces are in opposition to each other: the first condenses and solidifies matter to form the material world; the second raises the vibrational level of matter and provides the life force on which all living entities depend for their growth and development.

The Earth is in constant interplay with the two – the downwards and upwards, contracting and expanding, darkness and light (equivalent to the Chinese concepts of Yin and Yang). This interplay creates the ebb and flow of all our natural cycles: darkness and light, night and day, as well as the cycles of the seasons. It is the perfect balance of these forces that enables the material world to exist.

These forces also played their part in the long, slow process of creation which was to culminate in humanity. This began with the creation of the mineral kingdom which was fashioned from Spirit entities at a very low level of consciousness, virtually inert and unresponsive to stimuli. During this very early period the downward force was dominant. Eventually, through the action of the upwards life force, the Spiritual Hierarchy began to exert its influence on these beings. Those that were able to respond were activated to provide the building blocks of the next stage of creation, the plant kingdom. Those that could not remained as the mineral kingdom we know today.

The Second Stage: The Plant Kingdom

Plants range from very simple, near-mineral life forms to complex organisms with near-animal responses. Through their ability to respond to the forces in their environment, plants came to acquire invisible Etheric Bodies. This marked a crucially important development in evolution, since it enabled the interaction of the two opposing life forces to bring about the growth, fruition and decay of the plant.

Through the impulses from their Etheric Bodies, plants reached out into their environment to encompass the responsive beings of the mineral kingdom around them. These mineral beings were then raised to the same higher consciousness as the plant, and their activity helped to form the plant body by contributing the minerals essential to its growth. In this way the Earth, through the mineral kingdom, builds the body of the plant while the opposing force of the Sun encourages its growth.

Like all the kingdoms of nature, the plant kingdom exists between the spiritual and material worlds, reaching upwards towards the light and air, while rooted in the earth. It draws elements vital for growth from the mineral kingdom below, while taking in light and energy from the Sun and air above. Thus the interaction of the two opposing flows of energy produces the downward rooting and upward flowering of the plant.

The plant kingdom fulfilled one of the primary requirements of the second stage of creation:

sensitivity to the environment and the ability to respond to it. This was made possible by the acquisition of the Etheric Body – the energy body which surrounds and permeates all living things – which differentiated the plants from the purely physical mineral kingdom. It was the Etheric Body that enabled the Spirit beings from which plants were created to develop sensitivity and responsiveness to their environment.

This was an essential step towards the development of feelings and emotions, which would be vital for the creation of the human being. With their highly developed sensitivity, plants were the ideal vehicles in which to perfect all the positive emotional qualities, uninfluenced by the faculties of thinking and willing which colour the emotions in the human being.

Thus, over aeons of evolutionary development, the Spirit beings that animated certain plant species developed a resonance with particular human emotions; and within each of these species particular plants have evolved to the point where they can perfectly reflect a positive human emotion in a pure state.

With the establishment of the plant kingdom, half of creation was completed. This was a crucial stage in evolution: the entities then in existence had reached a stage of perfection which ensured the healthy, harmonious and perfectly balanced functioning of the whole natural world at that time. The Garden of Eden was established on Earth.

The Spirit beings of the Garden of Eden, or plant kingdom, have never left the Godhead and their divinity is still pure and perfect. Their role in nature is to hold the archetypal patterns of the plant kingdom and fashion the energy that holds these vibrating patterns into the physical structures we see all around us in the living world.

Because these beings have no individual Egos and are not hampered by material requirements, they are not exposed to the temptations of free will and materialism. They have thus been able to remain in a perfect state of harmony and balance. This makes it possible for humanity to turn to the plant kingdom for vibrational medicines (such as homoeopathic, herbal and flower remedies) to regain the balance and harmony appropriate to the needs of each individual.

The Third Stage: The Animal Kingdom

The plant has no independent control over its existence; life at the second stage therefore still lacked the opportunity for free will which would ultimately be necessary to the human being. For the next, third stage, the Spirit beings responsible for creation had to move beyond the plant-like state of consciousness, which simply reacts to the environment without thought or decision. This was achieved through the acquisition of a further energy body, the Astral Body, through which the faculties of thinking, feeling, and willing are experienced and controlled.

The Spirit beings responsible for the creation of the animal kingdom raised the level of physical life by building up a network of interrelating systems on which the human body would ultimately be based. These included a sophisticated nutritional system, and a nervous system that provided awareness not only of outward experiences but of internal events in terms of hunger, pain, sexual desire and so on. In this way, just as the plant kingdom perfected the human's emotional system, the animal kingdom perfected the physical.

Thus, through the development of the physical, chemical and nervous systems, together with the Astral Body, animals acquired awareness of both their internal and external worlds and of their responses to them, and also developed instinctive behaviour such as hunting and home-building. Finally, and very importantly, they developed the ability to relate to each other in social and family groups.

The Fourth Stage: Humanity

In the fourth stage the activities of the Spiritual Hierarchy finally reached their objective: the creation of the perfect vehicle for spiritual beings to live in the material world. Humans developed a higher level of consciousness than the animals, which gives them not only greater intelligence, but self-awareness in the form of the Ego, and the all-important faculties of independent thought and free will. And, as we saw in Chapter 1, we have five components: the Physical, Etheric and Astral Bodies, the Ego and the Higher Self, all of which have a part to play in our spiritual journey.

Humanity is therefore the end product of an unbroken chain of spiritual and physical evolution, without which we could never have come into being. *Thus we are linked, through our spiritual origins, with the rest of creation, and the quality of our material life depends on our recognising the part played by nature and working in co-operation with it.*

The Purpose of Human Existence

Human beings are ultimately spiritual beings, the outcome of a decision made at a high spiritual level. The whole purpose of creation is for individuals to learn and develop in a world of matter, until they are sufficiently spiritually evolved to return to their spiritual home. Our situation is like that of the biblical story of the Prodigal Son, who wanted to experience the materialism of the real world; after squandering his inheritance, he suffered all kinds of deprivations until – wiser and enlightened – he returned to his father's house, where he was made welcome.

The problem we face in life is the loss of contact with our spiritual origins resulting from physical incarnation. In order for spiritual beings to incarnate on Earth as humans, the Ego had to become split off from the rest of the Higher Self, the spiritual part of the Soul. It is possible – indeed, it is our task – to re-open and strengthen our spiritual connection through living in the material world. We can help ourselves by consciously working on our own development, with the help of the Higher Self.

Our Higher Selves, which live in the spiritual world, are aware of the purpose of creation. The Ego, however, may not be, and all too often the individual's lifestyle and behaviour conflict with this purpose. The disharmony this causes is experienced at a very deep level, often unknown to the individual but reflected by imbalances in the Astral Body. The more evolved the individual Ego the greater is the disharmony. This imbalance in turn distorts the Etheric Body, ultimately affecting our physical and emotional health. *Thus the conflict between our spiritual purpose and the life we lead is one of the main causes of chronic illness today.*

In order to restore some harmony, earthly life has been divided into two parts: at night, during the deepest periods of sleep, the Ego withdraws from the Physical Body, accompanied by the Astral Body. Together they visit the spiritual realm, the Astral Body's natural home, where they are rebalanced and restored to harmony by the Higher Self. The Ego is not generally aware of this support: on waking, it has no conscious recollection of the contact. The experience is, however, registered in the Astral Body, which is why we sometimes have flashes of awareness or understanding not gained from our everyday experiences.

Although our contact with our Higher Selves can initially be tenuous, and often remains so, the connection is never totally broken. This connection is like a cord; the stronger the cord the more in touch and evolved the person, the thinner and more thread-like the cord the less in touch, and the more unhappy or even hellish their existence. There are a number of ways of strengthening that link and becoming consciously aware of the role of our Higher Selves; we shall be looking at some of these in Chapter 7.

Thus we are equipped to work towards our ultimate purpose, which is to use our free will to develop our spirituality during our physical existence, to the point at which we can return permanently to the spiritual realm. Human beings are at a fairly low level of the Spiritual Hierarchy, and every Ego has to work out its destiny slowly through many incarnations. At the end of each life, when we return to the spiritual realm, we have the opportunity to reflect on the lessons of the previous life and on those we have yet to learn.

After death, the experiences of the Etheric Body are absorbed by the Soul. This process has been described by some people who have gone through near-death experiences as the experience of witnessing their whole previous life. During the time we spend in the spiritual realm between incarnations, we reflect on and learn from the experiences of our last life. When it is time to prepare for the next incarnation, the Soul creates a new Astral and Etheric Body, whose form will be based on the lessons needed for the Ego's spiritual development. This is why some people are born with special gifts or severe handicaps – not as a reward or punishment for past-life actions, but to provide the Ego with the challenges necessary to further its evolution.

Humanity and the Two Forces

The most important influence in our spiritual evolution is our constant exposure to the formative downward and upward forces that are constantly involved in creation. It is by means of the downwards force that the Spiritual Hierarchy has brought the Ego into physical existence on Earth. This also controls the first part of the individual's lifetime as it brings the Ego into full incarnation, through birth and childhood to adulthood. At this stage, the downward energy becomes progressively exhausted, and the upstream takes over, eventually taking the Ego back to the spiritual realm at death.

During every single lifetime, the individual is faced with finding a balance between these two forces. The downward force tends to direct people's attention entirely to the physical world and its materialism, to the detriment of their spirituality. The positive upward stream draws people to focus purely on the spiritual life, which can make them unrealistic and escapist, whereas in fact our destiny can only be fulfilled through acting in the material world.

However, the more the Ego tries to use its own resources to progress materially, the more cut off it becomes from its true, spiritual task. This is the stage we are at today: human beings have made huge technical advances, but the majority are unaware of their real role in the plan of evolution. As a result, both humanity and the environment are in a state of disharmony which is expressed in individuals as disease, unhappiness and chronic illness, and in society as crime, warfare, ecological problems, and the general suffering that pervades the planet. To reverse this state of affairs, we need to understand what we are really here for, and learn to work with and harmonise the two forces.

Finding the balance between the two is the key to continuous and perfect health. We have to grasp them both, and use them as the basis for developing our spirituality and for making our own contribution to carrying evolution further forward.

3. *Huna Beliefs and the Three Selves*

As we have seen, the human being consists of much more than is apparent to our everyday senses. The Physical Body is surrounded and interpenetrated by energy fields and systems, the importance of which are increasingly recognised by complementary therapists and healers. It is significant that the Kahunas, the doctor-priests of Polynesia, knew of similar systems thousands of years ago, including the existence of energy bodies and the Higher Self.

Through similarities in their language and symbols, it seems clear that the Huna philosophy and practices had their origins in Ancient Egypt. In Polynesia, the Kahunas were the custodians of this very ancient tradition; they were miracle-workers, revered by the local people who constantly sought their advice and help on life problems, and particularly on matters of health and healing. For centuries the Kahunas passed their teachings on to each generation so that their philosophy remained pure and uncorrupted.

The Huna tradition remained integral to the Hawaiian way of life until the end of the last century, when Western missionaries arrived and, as elsewhere in the world, progressively replaced the ancient native beliefs with Christian concepts. They outlawed the practice of Kahuna magic, and in time, the old Huna beliefs and practices succumbed to Christianity and died away, except in some small communities in remote islands. However, they have never been completely lost. Today, the increasing interest in such traditions has led to a revival of the Kahuna wisdom, and Western healers and therapists regularly visit Hawaii to train in Kahuna healing techniques which address the body, mind and spirit.

Long before the development of modern psychology the Kahunas knew that the human being was not a single unit. Only recently in the West have psychological pioneers like Sigmund Freud and Carl Jung recognised that the mind encompasses other, deeper levels than conscious, every-day thinking, while today transpersonal psychologists also recognise the existence of a Higher, or Spiritual Self. Very much longer ago, the Kahunas saw the individual as made up of three selves, separate but interdependent: this knowledge contributed radically to their ability to diagnose and heal physical and emotional illness.

The Make-up of the Human Being

According to Huna philosophy, the human being is made of several components:

> The Lower, or Subconscious Self – (Feeling Self)
>
> The Middle, or Conscious Self – (Rational Self)
>
> The Higher, or Superconscious Self
>
> The Etheric Body – the energy body of the Subconscious Self
>
> The Astral Body – the energy body of the Conscious Self
>
> The Physical Body
>
> Mana – The energy or vital force of the individual. (Referred to as *prana* in India, and in China and Japan as *Qi/Ki*)

In order to become fully developed human and spiritual beings, we need to acknowledge the existence of all these aspects of ourselves, and in particular to get to know the first three selves so that they can cooperate in our development.

These three selves have been given different names by various researchers in this field. To Max Freedom Long, the discoverer of Kahuna lore, they were the Lower, Middle and Higher Selves; Serge King, a contemporary writer on Kahuna wisdom, calls them 'Heart, Mind and Spirit'; they have also been called the Subconscious, Conscious and Superconscious Selves. The two selves constituting what we have earlier described as the Ego have also been referred to as the Child Self and the Adult Self, and the Feeling Self and the Thinking

Self. I have opted to call them the Feeling Self and the Rational Self, which seems to approach most clearly the Kahuna meaning.

The Feeling Self

Max Freedom Long calls this the Lower Self. It corresponds to a large degree with what psychologists call the Subconscious mind, and is also strongly connected to the Physical Body. Centred in the solar plexus chakra, it controls our involuntary bodily processes and everything but the voluntary muscles.

The energy body which envelops the Feeling Self is the Etheric Body, the blueprint of every cell, tissue and fluid in the Physical Body; it can slide into and out of the Physical Body, and it impregnates every part of the body and brain. All our thoughts, impressions and actions are stored as memory in that part of the Etheric Body which impregnates the brain, which thus becomes the repository of all our past experiences, and determines our individuality.

Very importantly, the Feeling Self is the seat of the emotions. Love, hate, greed and fear all arise from the Feeling Self in the form of strong emotions which can affect the will and the behaviour of the Rational Self, forcing it to share the feeling or to react to it. When these emotions are negative they may overwhelm us or lead us astray.

The Feeling Self receives sensory impressions

through the five senses, and presents them to the
Rational Self for explanation and action, if required.
It also records every impression and every thought
we ever have. Thus memory is a key function
of the Feeling Self. In addition, the Etheric Body is
very sensitive to thought, so that if distorted
thoughts are held in the mind for any length of
time, the Etheric Body also becomes distorted, eventually leading to the impairment of the Physical
Body.

The Feeling Self responds quickly to the
Rational Self's demands to recall memories and
experiences, and the Rational Self then uses this
information to deal with day-to-day events and
situations. This partnership can work successfully only when the memories and experiences
have been properly understood and validated
by the Rational Self before being stored away.
For the Feeling Self lacks judgment. It acts rather
like the memory of a computer, building up mental
and physical habits, and automatic behaviour
patterns and reactions. It often holds mistaken
ideas which have not been rationalised by the
Rational Self: the Rational Self may not even be
aware that they exist. These in turn develop into
fixations and complexes which can lead to major
problems.

This process starts in childhood. The Rational
Self only starts to reason in a limited way around
the age of seven, and does not develop adequate
understanding or full rational control of its thoughts

and actions until the late teens – even later in some individuals. It is at this early stage of life that great damage can be inflicted which will surface later on.

Religious teachings, moral values, family customs and beliefs, social and racial conventions are instilled into children by well-meaning adults. In this way dubious moral values and social conventions (such as prejudice of various kinds, and unthought-out religious dogmas) are accepted as truths. The same applies to personal criticisms and judgments. If a small child is consistently told that it is stupid, naughty, deceitful, unacceptable, and so on, the Feeling Self will store these judgments as fact. The child's Rational Self is not yet developed enough to question this false information, which is then permanently stored and continually acted upon, unless something is done to change the programme. As a result, many people suffer in later life from faulty beliefs about themselves: these cause a great deal of illness and emotional suffering in the world today.

The Rational Self

The Rational Self (Long calls it the Middle Self) is the Conscious Self, the part of the mind we are aware of in ordinary daily life. It is the centre of the sensations, thoughts and feelings received through the Physical and Astral Bodies which enable us to act effectively in the material world; its energy body, the Astral Body, is located between the throat and brow chakras, and comprises the faculties of thinking, feeling and willing. It is the Astral Body that instigates our actions.

The Rational Self speaks, reasons, controls our voluntary actions, and also uses intuition to know and experience our material environment. Its primary role is to relate the body to the outside world through our five senses. While the data from our sensory systems is processed through the Feeling Self, only the Rational Self can put this information together to form a coherent picture.

The Rational Self has only a short-term memory; to make sense of the world it has to rely heavily on the Feeling Self for memories of past experiences. It has, however, the ability to reason, and to initiate decisions. One of its most important functions is to give clear directions to the Feeling Self.

The Higher Self

The Higher Self is the highest form of human consciousness. It is located outside the Physical Body above the crown chakra (at the top of the head), and is connected to the body by a golden cord rooted in the physical heart. Unlike the first two selves, the energy body which houses it does not interpenetrate the Physical Body.

The Higher Self accompanies the Feeling and Rational Selves throughout life, as guardian, guide

and inspiration. It does not interfere unless specifically asked; it observes the principle of free will, so
that the true purpose of our period in the material
world can be experienced. It can be contacted
through prayer and meditation.

The Kahunas recognised the existence of
even higher spiritual beings, beyond human consciousness, but since they were unable to make
direct contact with them, they made their prayers
to the Higher Self which can call on these beings
on our behalf.

To the Kahunas, the Higher Self was the
'utterly trustworthy parental Spirit', combining both
mother and father. It watches kindly over us, and
communicates with us during sleep and in meditation. Because we have free will it cannot intervene directly in our lives unless we ask it to: but
when we give it the opportunity, it has the power
to guide and advise us at all times.

The Physical Body

Together with the Etheric and Astral bodies, the
Physical Body constitutes the vehicle through
which we exist, have experiences, and act in the
material world. It is also a physical manifestation of
the acquired attitudes and habits of the Feeling and
Rational Selves. This means that its appearance
and state of health can be altered by changing our
attitudes, habits and behaviour.

Energy

According to the Huna tradition there are three main forms of energy, which vibrate at different frequencies and which relate to the Feeling Self, the Rational Self and the Higher Self. (These three frequencies are known in other systems. In Chinese philosophy, they are known as *Qing* (ching), *Qi* (chi) and *Shen*. Similarly, healers recognise three levels of healing energy – usually termed magnetic, etheric, and spiritual.)

Mana – the Energy of the Individual

Mana is the primary energy, the energy of the Feeling or Subconscious Self, vibrating at the lowest level. It constitutes our vital energy or life force, and is created by the interaction of the food we eat and the oxygen we breathe. It is essential for the maintenance and day-to-day operation of the Physical Body: it keeps us alive and enables us to heal ourselves. It animates the circulation of our blood, our digestive processes and the electrical activity of the nervous system. All these essential life processes are made possible by the continuous movement of Mana, which flows through the body like an electric current, and around it like a magnetic field.

For good physical health the right amount and production of Mana is essential for one's bodily requirements, together with a strong circulation of Mana through the body. Factors that upset this vital function are poor nutrition and bad eating habits, poor breathing, inner stress and negative mental and emotional attitudes.

Mana-Mana

This is the energy of the Rational or Conscious Self, and is of a higher vibrational nature than Mana. It is important to us because it provides the energy for our willpower, which in turn activates our desires and intentional actions. As the tool of the Rational Self it allows us to have free will, but since it is related to our thinking it can have both positive and negative components and effects.

Mana-Loa

This is the energy of the Higher Self. Its vibrational level is much higher than that of the first two energies, and it acts in a very different way: this is the force involved in prayer and healing, which we shall be examining more closely in later chapters.

Thus there are three dimensions to all of us, and we live in all three dimensions simultaneously. Each of the three Selves exists in a specific realm of consciousness, the natural, the human, and the divine. Each is dependent on the other two for its own growth, so cooperation between them is essential.

4. The Causes of Illness

The challenge for all of us, and the way to perfect health, is to maintain a harmonious relationship between the triple aspects of ourselves: the Feeling, Rational and Higher Selves, and the Physical, Etheric and Astral Bodies. It is not only the Physical Body that needs to be nourished, exercised and rested. Our spiritual and emotional selves, which are linked to the Astral Body, also need to be attended to. Paying attention to the spiritual purpose of our lives, and resolving the emotional problems which often prevent us from fulfilling that true purpose, are vitally important if we are to evolve. Our lives need to include a balance between all these areas – something very few people manage. Most of us disrupt our potential harmony by the way we lead our lives, and one of the lessons to be learned in our current incarnation is the crucial importance of the need for balance.

The difficulty in achieving this was provided
for in creation by the division of life into waking and
sleeping; during deep sleep, when the Rational
Self is withdrawn, our Higher Selves attempt to
restore harmony without interference from our
consciousness. But on awakening, the Rational
Self reasserts control and the whole cycle begins
again. If, after some time, a more regular state of
balance is not established, the resulting disharmonies can manifest as illness. How long this
takes, and how severe the disharmony experienced by any individual before serious illness
arises, will vary according both to physical and
genetic factors and to the individual's state of
spiritual evolution.

Physical Factors in Illness

The body is formed and structured from energy; it
is the distortion of this energy that creates illness.
The discomfort experienced by the Soul whose
Ego is going awry is reflected by imbalances in the
Astral Body which in turn distort the Etheric Body,
ultimately affecting the Physical. The body is then
vulnerable to bacteria, viruses, pollution, and so on.

The causes of disharmony originating at the
conscious and physical level include malnutrition,
over-eating or drinking, an unbalanced diet, addictions, lack of exercise, and poor breathing. Accidents, of course, can also cause physical damage,
and when this is serious the effects may be carried

through to the Astral Body. And drugs and medicines intended to be therapeutic produce side effects which cause disharmony, particularly when taken over an extended period.

As for recreational drugs, their use temporarily displaces the Astral Body, leading to the so-called trip, in which hallucinatory experiences are in fact glimpses of the Astral Plane (the realm between the physical and the spiritual). The same phenomenon occurs with the over-use of alcohol, which of course is also a drug. The danger is that once the effects of the drug have worn off, the Astral Body remains partially displaced and out of balance; it is then also vulnerable to negative influences which can affect the balance of the mind and give rise to uncharacteristic thoughts and behaviour. It is this displacement of the Astral Body that causes withdrawal symptoms, and the need for more of the drug to restore so-called normality to the user.

Disharmonies that are physical in origin can and need to be dealt with by eliminating the physical cause; if they are allowed to continue unchecked, their effects can penetrate to higher levels. But, except in extremely bad social conditions, it is rare for illness to be purely physical in cause. Most of us have choices in life. If we choose to adopt unhealthy habits, our choice is usually accompanied by a negative attitude – conscious or unconscious – that contributes to our lack of self-care.

There is also a genetic factor in physical disease, of which modern medicine is aware. Heart disease, cancer, and other serious conditions are known to have an hereditary component. Medical research today is discovering new facts about our complicated body chemistry and how it works, and is even identifying the individual genes responsible for the more serious chronic illnesses. However, science has not yet addressed the reason why humanity has these potentially hostile genes in the first place, or what activates them to trigger serious illness in many sufferers.

What the medical profession does not teach us – and would probably laugh at – is the concept that our genetic system has a spiritual dimension. In fact, our genetic make-up represents an identikit picture of our selves, our strengths and our weaknesses, together with the attitudes acquired over many incarnations by our Feeling and Rational Selves.

For example, if a person dies of cancer without successfully identifying and dealing with the cause of the disharmony underlying that cancer, this will be retained in the Soul-body after death. The gene responsible for cancer will then appear in that person's make-up in their next incarnation. Likewise, if someone has an addictive gene, unless the addiction is faced and overcome, that genetic propensity will be carried through into the next life. In fact, all the genes responsible for potential negative conditions will continue to form part of our genetic package until we have addressed and eliminated each of those conditions.

The Emotional and Spiritual Causes of Illness

The causes of disharmony originating at the Sub-conscious and Etheric Level are negative thoughts, repressed emotions such as fear, sorrow, anger and rage, and negative attitudes and behaviours. These conditions cause the Etheric Body to become significantly unbalanced and blocked, and if they are not corrected serious chronic illness will even-tually manifest in the Physical Body.

Practitioners of both natural and conventional medicine are increasingly aware of the role of stress and unhappiness in creating ill-health. The spiritual dimension of medicine goes even further: stress itself is often the consequence of an unrecognised but deep-rooted spiritual unease caused by the con-flict between the Ego and the Soul. Unfortunately, Western medicine and religion have no all-inclusive system enabling us to integrate our physical, emotional and spiritual selves into both the material and the spiritual worlds around us.

A very common cause of inner conflict is the difference between the way the Ego wants life to be and the way it actually is. When life is as we want it, we experience pleasure and joy, which are health enhancing in themselves. Conversely, the disconnection between our spiritual nature and everyday living is often experienced as a dissatis-faction with life, a sense that something is missing – which is, of course, the case.

Unfortunately, people tend to seek this missing

part in material achievements and sources of satis-faction which are not ultimately satisfying. And when the Ego is not fulfilling the task for which it came into this life, when the individual's 'mission statement' – their life plan – has been lost sight of, there is a state of turmoil between the Ego and that part of our Soul which is connected with our Higher Self, which sooner or later affects the Physical Body.

The Meaning of Death

Losing sight of one's 'mission statement' is, I believe, one reason for premature death – either through serious illness or through accidents such as car crashes. Let us be clear: these are not visited on us as a punishment for failure. Rather, it seems that when people's lives are not working as they should, and may even have gone very wrong, they may have a subconscious desire to return to the starting post and begin again, rather than con-tinuing to erode their spirituality.

The decision to return to base takes place at a very deep level, guided by the Soul and the Higher Self. In most cases of terminal illness in which this is a factor, the individual Ego is not conscious of taking a decision to abort its present incarnation and return to the Spirit realm. This is different from suicide, when the individual consciously makes a decision which is often escapist and can have serious spiritual consequences.

At the same time, events that cut lives short –
which may seem tragic in human terms – tend to
have widespread effects beyond the individual life
and death. One is to provide all those people linked
to the person concerned with an opportunity for
their own spiritual development or expansion of
consciousness. A serious illness can give family,
friends and carers an opening for expressing love
and caring in a deeper way than before. Sometimes the ripples spread very wide: the death in
1997 of Diana, Princess of Wales affected a whole
nation, giving people pause for thought about the
values of our society.

Of course, another reason for apparently premature death is that one has successfully completed one's purpose for this particular incarnation.
This can sometimes be seen with the deaths of
children and young people. Often regarded as a
meaningless waste, they may in fact be important
contributions to the emotional development of the
parents, or to an increased awareness of society's
treatment of the young.

Most people, of course, live out their allotted
span, particularly so long as they have a role to
fulfil – in their work, as a husband or wife, or as a
parent. But not everyone fulfils their spiritual role,
and it is possible that much illness in middle and
old age would be prevented if people were able to
listen to what their symptoms of ill-health were
telling them. For serious illness usually has an
important purpose.

The Causes
of Illness

The Message of Illness

Illnesses are actually a part of our self-healing process; many of them are caused by the efforts of the body and mind to resolve inner conflicts. The Feeling Self is quick to recognise any kind of imbalance in the body-mind system, and will try to communicate this imbalance to the Rational Self so that something can be done about it. Its customary method of communication is to produce signs and symptoms of illness; at an early stage these may manifest as stress symptoms, perhaps not very specific in nature, or as minor accidents. If, at this stage, the Rational Self takes note and acts sensibly, the process can be brought to a halt and health restored.

Stress is often at the root of health problems that we may not recognise as stress-related. Our physical responses to short-term stress are a natural way of preparing the body to take appropriate action (by producing adrenalin and raising the heart-beat, for instance). It is when stress becomes chronic that it is harmful, eventually leading to malfunction of the body's chemical and nervous systems, and eventually to the breakdown of the immune system which defends us against serious disease.

Stress is often caused by unresolved emotional problems like repressed anger, constant anxiety, unexpressed grief, and fear. Ignoring or suppressing these emotions can have profound effects. Negative feelings and behaviour patterns react on the Etheric Body so that it loses vitality; since the Etheric Body is the blueprint of the Physical, this loss of vitality is then reflected physically.

We all pay attention to the everyday communications of the body – hunger, thirst, sensitivity to heat and cold, the need to evacuate and to sleep, and so on. But we are not all aware of the signals sent by the Feeling Self to the Rational Self, to warn it that action must be taken before serious illness ensues.

All too often the Rational Self is unwilling to listen to the messages of the Feeling Self, or simply unaware that it is being given a serious warning. Busy with material preoccupations, the Rational Self will try to override these early-warning signals by taking a pill and trying to 'pull itself together' while it gets on with its daily business. However, if this continues for long enough, the Physical Body will eventually start to malfunction and real disease will take hold.

When a person begins to experience symptoms and fails to understand their message, they are more likely to see themselves as the victims of illness than that there is something fundamentally wrong with their lifestyle. If the Rational Self persists in believing in the illness, the Feeling Self will eventually believe in it too (since it is always influenced by the Rational Self), and will start to manifest something more serious.

Unless the cause is found and the relevant problems dealt with, the immune system will begin to fail and the process of illness will take its inevitable course until the individual becomes chronically sick. This can take time, and it may take a serious illness such as heart disease or cancer before the sufferer starts to re-think their real purpose in life.

The Rational Self, being only aware of the conscious world, will realise that the body is suffering, but will rarely understand why. Illness is still widely regarded as something visited on us from outside, rather than the result of our own internal processes. The medical profession and patients alike are only too willing to blame bacteria, viruses and the environment; some people, too, see illness as an imposition, or a test or even a punishment. Seriously ill patients often ask, 'Why me? What did I do to deserve this?' In fact, punishment is not a factor in illness – though responsibility often is.

To take responsibility for one's own illness involves recognising the role played by the Rational and Feeling Selves in causing or prolonging it; we need to understand that the illness is the body's way of letting us know that we have unresolved problems. Accidents, too, can be a way of drawing our attention to the fact that all is not well in our life; sometimes minor accidents precede serious ones, as if giving us warning that there is a problem to be dealt with. To restore our health, we need to resolve these conflicts. Even though we are already aware of many of them, there are often deep-seated underlying factors of which we are less aware.

What we can learn from the Kahunas is the vital importance of integrating the three selves, the Feeling, Rational, and Higher Selves. The purpose of illness is to draw our attention to the conflicts and imbalances between the three, and to the fears and guilts that prevent them form working together harmoniously. By eliminating these, we can enable the three selves to work in cooperation, bringing balance and wellbeing into our daily lives.

The Power of Thought

All our involuntary body systems – including our nervous, circulatory, muscular and digestive systems and, very importantly, our immune system – are under the direct control of the Feeling Self; in Kahuna terms, the Feeling Self is the manager of the Physical Body, and is also closely linked with the Etheric Body. In addition, the Feeling Self is responsible for our memories, thoughts and emotional reactions, and is strongly affected by them. When these are negative and painful, the conflict it experiences is inevitably reflected in the Physical Body.

The operation of our bodily systems is therefore influenced very directly by the way we think and feel. Negative thoughts cause blocks and distortions in the healthy flow of energy and reduce the ability of the immune system to ward off and fight disease. Positive thoughts, by contrast, produce positive energy and stimulate the immune system.

It is important to understand that thoughts are a form of energy, which becomes concentrated into what are called 'thought-forms'. According to the Kahunas, thought-forms have substance, and shape; they are active energy influences and, once born, can rule our lives. Even at a subconscious level, they still have power over us.

If you dwell on a thought continually, you not only become accustomed to it: you give it greater power and energy. It begins to take precedence over other thoughts, conditioning the rest of your thinking and your way of life. When more and more power is given to a negative thought over time, the thinker's own energy is depleted; this is a common cause of depression, as well as of chronic illness.

The Kahunas believed that the negative thought-forms which live within us impede our ability to function normally. Negative thoughts interpose themselves between the requests and commands of the Rational Self and the actions of the Feeling Self; they act as saboteurs, limiting our true abilities and potentials. They are often focused on fears and conflicts, remembrances of negative experiences and old hurts.

The Feeling Self and our Belief Systems

Why do we persist in thinking thoughts that may harm us? At the root of our thinking process there is always a set of beliefs, which are often both negative and erroneous. Negative belief systems are not only a cause of illness, but are at the root of a great deal of human misery; they underlie social problems such as failure, poor job performance, divorce, addictions, criminal behaviour and much more. Most faulty beliefs about ourselves and our environment are acquired in childhood; instilled into the Feeling Self by well-meaning adults, they become part of our accepted world view until we decide, or are forced to re-consider, their validity.

Our beliefs act as a filter, causing us to see the world differently from the way it really is. Negative beliefs can screen out positive information so that we only perceive what we believe to be true. A good example of this is prejudice; bigoted people who regularly express negative views on religion, race, skin colour, and so on, are generally unable to accept objective evidence that they may be wrong, and will focus on any events that seem to prove them right.

For example, if parents frequently tell a small child that he or she is stupid or naughty, the child – who cannot yet form an independent judgment – has no option but to believe them. Beliefs instilled at an early age by powerful authority figures become part of the child's make-up and personality, and the child will start to act accordingly. These beliefs are then likely to be reinforced, over and over again, both by past memories and present events. Poor exam results, criticism from teachers or employers, or put-downs from fellow students or colleagues, will be seen as proof that the individual really is stupid or unworthy and will discourage them from trying to see themselves in a different light.

Faulty beliefs like these interfere with the body's ability to function normally, and diminish its ability to maintain health. When we live by faulty beliefs we have considerable conflict in our lives. But since we dislike conflict and pain, we often either suppress our feelings or project them outside ourselves – blaming other people or conditions for our own unhappiness.

Guilt is another major cause of stress and illness, whether instilled by religious teachings or by over-critical parents, and whether or not it is deserved. Well-intentioned parents may have life-goals for their children which they are unsuited for, or unable to achieve. Many people experience conflict between the religious beliefs they were brought up with, or the expectations of their families, and the way they themselves want to live. Trying to follow one's parents' path rather than one's own destiny can create enormous inner conflict, while going against parental wishes can equally leave a lasting and painful sense of guilt.

Some religious and cultural groups still preach doom-laden dogmas against 'sins' which other cultures regard as normal activities. This can have lasting effects on psychological health. If you believe that sin is inevitably followed by retribution, your life will be shadowed by the fear of retribution – either in this life or the next. Few doctors recognise the destructive elements of some of these religious teachings, or realise the extent to which religious dogma causes chronic illness in the community. There is no medical formula for dealing with guilt, and it can take years of psychotherapy to overcome the emotional damage it causes. The Kahunas, however, in their healing rituals, laid great emphasis on freeing the sick from the damaging effects of guilt for real or imagined sins; we will be describing these further in Chapter 6 on page 77.

Guilt also contributes to a sense of personal unworthiness, an inability to love oneself. This is tragic, for love is the protector: it energises and maintains the immune system. Hence, when there is an absence of self-love and self-respect, the immune system, as well as the other bodily systems, tends to be below par. Other problems may well follow: alcoholism, excessive smoking and eating disorders all suggest that there is a significant breach in self-love and self-value.

If we have allowed guilt or other destructive thought complexes to take root in our Feeling Self, it is very likely that we will experience illness at some point. If, on the other hand, we can locate and eliminate these factors, we can improve our chances for a healthy, trouble-free life. For this, we need the cooperation of the Rational Self, which makes our decisions about how we live.

Throughout our development from infancy to adulthood, we are bathed by both positive and negative thought processes and belief systems. Ultimately, every individual must decide which to accept and which to reject. When someone accepts more negative than positive ideas, they end up with a negative mind-set. Conversely, accepting more positive than negative ideas will give them a positive outlook on life.

Thought-forms have energy, and energy cannot be destroyed. It can, however, be transformed. The Kahunas maintained that once a thought-form is created, it can be transformed or replaced with a new, healthier thought. Faulty beliefs can be thrown away and changed at any time, but in order to do this effectively *the Feeling Self needs to be reprogrammed to accept the new belief.* We will be discussing how to do this in Chapter 5.

5. *The Treatment of Illness*

The medical profession, and probably most patients, consider that once all the physical symptoms of an illness have been eliminated, the patient can be pronounced cured. In the main this is achieved by the chemical suppression of symptoms, together with the patient's natural powers of recovery. Visiting the doctor and being prescribed treatment can in themselves trigger the healing process. In fact, it could be said that the real healer is the patient, together with the power of his or her beliefs. Taking medication acts as a kind of ritual and reassurance, and is often understood by patients as a symbol of the doctor's power to get them better. In other words, what cures them is the Feeling Self. By seeking and accepting medical help, the person is giving a clear, decisive command to their Feeling Self to get them better.

This is fine when the illness is minor and temporary, as is often the case; many of us recover from transitory illnesses without further problems. It is when these recur or become chronic that we need to take serious note. In these cases, the type of recovery just described does not deal with the true cause of the problem, which usually lies beyond the physical. If there is a deep inner conflict, although health may apparently be restored, a permanent cure cannot be achieved until the underlying cause has been discovered and treated. Failing this, the condition may return in a more serious form, possibly after many years. So it is important to take note of the symptoms of illness at an early stage, and ask ourselves what message they are trying to convey.

The common cold is a very good example of the body's built-in early-warning system in action. We all tend to build up toxins in our bodies because of the nature of our lifestyles; for most people this unfortunately happens on a fairly regular basis. The classic symptoms of the common cold are a raised temperature, sweating, sneezing, coughing, and a runny nose: these are nature's way of getting rid of toxins. Rather than trying to suppress a cold by taking remedies, it is best to allow it to run its natural course, accompanied by rest and drinking plenty of fluids; this reduces the toxins to an acceptable level. Thus the cold serves as a cleansing process which prevents a build-up of toxins from bringing about a more serious illness.

It is obviously even more important to take note of the underlying message of more serious or debilitating symptoms, particularly if they recur regularly.

Natural Therapies

The natural or complementary therapies at least avoid the side-effects of medical drugs. They also take into account the deeper aspects of health and illness: most are based on the principle that human beings consist of more than their Physical Bodies.

As we have seen, disease comes about through disharmony resulting from hereditary, environmental, psychosomatic and spiritual factors. Good holistic therapists recognise all of these, and will treat individuals as individuals (unlike conventional medicine which tends to approach disease as though it existed independently of the patient). The majority acknowledge the role played by our thoughts, emotions and belief systems in health and sickness, while dealing with physical problems through diet, manipulation, the use of herbs, and so on. And nowadays a wide range of therapies address the patient's energy system.

Many complementary therapists recognise the existence of the chakras, the centres of energy which have long been integral to Indian and Tibetan medicine. These centres of whirling energy (chakra means 'wheel' in Sanskrit) are found in alignment between the crown of the head and the base of the spine; running through them and from them is an interpenetrating network of channels of etheric energy.

The chakras control the activity of the Etheric Body. They also govern the activity of particular physical organs, endocrine glands and internal systems, as well as our emotional and spiritual activity. When they are out of balance (under- or over-active, or blocked in some way), the person will be out of balance physically and emotionally. Certain of the natural therapies are particularly successful in restoring this balance.

A good natural therapist will be aware that an illness may be emotionally based, and may therefore respond best to a psychological approach or counselling. Other conditions may require a physical or other appropriate natural form of treatment to restore the harmonious functioning of the Physical and Etheric Bodies. Some will require more than one approach, and many natural therapies address body, mind and even spirit simultaneously.

A good example is acupuncture. This ancient Chinese therapy is based on the network of invisible channels, called meridians, which carry energy through the body. The meridians are connected with specific organs and body systems, and also with particular emotions. For example, the liver meridian is related both to the physical liver and to anger; the kidney meridian is associated with fear, and so on. The energy system connects the physical and the emotional: an imbalance in one will create an imbalance in the other. Likewise, correcting the one will help to correct the other.

If a person lives a harmonious and creative life, according to their level of spiritual development, their energies will circulate freely. However, in people who suffer from stress or frustrations which block the energy flow, the imbalance of energy can bring about a malfunctioning of the physical system. The skilled acupuncturist aims to restore a harmonious flow of energy throughout the body by applying fine needles or heat to specific points on the meridians. This has the effect of sedating over-active energy or encouraging stagnant energy to flow. Once the energy moves more harmoniously the patient experiences not only relief from physical symptoms but a greater sense of inner harmony and relaxation.

All complementary therapies focus on encouraging the patient's own self-healing powers, whereas conventional medicine tends to suppress symptoms with drugs. These in turn may suppress the immune or other systems, leading to debilitating side effects. I have been particularly involved with three forms of natural therapy, whose effects I have seen for myself over and over again: Homoeopathy, the Bach Flower Remedies, and Etheric Healing. Let us take a closer look at how and why they work.

Homoeopathy

The name 'homoeopathy' is derived from the Greek word '*homoios*', meaning 'like'. It is the practice of treating like with like: that is, treating an illness with a substance that is known to produce the same symptoms in a healthy person as those displayed by the sick person. Orthodox medical opinion believes that the symptoms are *caused* by the illness, and responds by prescribing medicine designed to eliminate them. Homoeopathy, by contrast, sees the symptoms as the body's reaction as its attempts to fight and overcome the illness; it therefore seeks to stimulate this reaction rather than suppress it. Homoeopathic remedies thus help the person to regain health by encouraging the body's natural forces of recovery.

Homoeopathic remedies are made from plant, mineral, animal and other natural products. They are made through a process of successive dilution and succussion of the starting material – succussion, or potentisation, as it is often called, is the vigorous shaking of the dilutant after each dilution. This diluting process is continued to a stage at which not even a molecule of the original substance is present in the remedy – one reason why the medical profession is sceptical about homoeopathy, despite the evidence of clinical research. In these extreme dilutions certain normally poisonous plants and mineral materials, known to produce the symptoms of particular illnesses, are often very efficacious remedies, based on the 'like cures like' concept.

There is also an energy factor in homoeo-pathic remedies. In Chapter 2 we saw how all matter and all plants comprise spiritual beings at various levels of consciousness and spiritual evolvement: this has an immensely important bearing on the quality and effectiveness of certain medicines.

Allopathic medicines – those used in conven-tional medicine – are usually made from chemical compounds, often originally derived from natural sources (aspirin, for example, comes from the willow). In its natural form, the active ingredient – the ingredient that does the healing work – con-stitutes only part of the total plant: plants which have a medical application have been endowed with a natural antidote to any potential side effects. This is one reason why herbal medicines are so effective, particularly when prescribed by a skilled medical herbalist: they make use of the whole plant. In allopathic medicine, by contrast, once the active ingredient has been identified by the pharmaceuti-cal industry, it is usually isolated, analysed, and chemically reproduced. This is what gives rise to side effects which nature did not intend.

Once the active ingredient has been treated in this way, the spiritual beings associated with the original plant are no longer present in the com-pound, which is therefore inactive from the spiritual or energy point of view. The drug is directed to the physical plane only, and cannot affect the patient's Etheric and Astral Bodies, which is where the

The
Treatment
of Illness

correction needs to take place. In the Physical Body it will have only a temporary effect, and as this wears off the condition often returns: sufferers from complaints like high blood pressure, arthritis, and so on are often on drugs for their whole lives. They may also have to take further pills to counteract the side effects.

Homoeopathy, by contrast, uses the whole plant or substance, incorporating the spiritual beings that went into its creation, together with the life-force energies that formed it. Through the diluting and potentising stages these spiritual beings, and the associated life-forces, are progressively and harmoniously released, freeing their spiritual qualities. Since the life-force energies are the same forces that bring about the harmonious activity of the living world, they can be very efficacious in treating malfunctioning systems in the human body.

When homoeopathic remedies are taken, they are absorbed by the patient and raised up through the successive levels of the Physical, Etheric and Astral Bodies. During this process the spiritual qualities pertaining to each plant or substance become conscious and active, contributing their vibrational energy to the patient. If the remedy corresponds to the type and level of disharmony in the patient's energy bodies, it will correct the imbalances at all levels.

In addition, homoeopathy concentrates on treating the individual person rather than the disease. Identifying the correct remedies for reasonably serious conditions requires the involvement of an experienced homoeopathic practitioner, who will take into account not just the person's symptoms but their personality, physical make-up, habits and lifestyle. Once the correct course of treatment has been completed, the patient's system will be rebalanced and restored to harmony: when the vibrational distortion in the Etheric Body is corrected, physical symptoms will automatically disappear.

The Bach Flower Remedies

Flower remedies have evolved in this century to heal and balance emotional and spiritual qualities. The pioneer in this field was Dr Edward Bach (1886–1936), a Welsh physician and homoeopath. He spent his life seeking ever more refined methods of healing, particularly of the emotions, which he considered the main cause of ill-health. Constantly experimenting on himself, he discovered thirty-eight remedies, most of them based on trees and flowers, which have the potential to heal thirty-eight negative states of mind, including fear, loneliness, anger, and so on. The majority are made simply by floating the flower heads in spring water in full sunlight. The water becomes imbued with the energy of the plant, and is then bottled and preserved with a little brandy, to be further diluted when taken.

The Bach Flower Remedies, which first appeared in the 1930s, have become popular worldwide, chiefly by word of mouth. How do these gentle remedies restore emotional harmony? As we saw in Chapter 2, when the plant kingdom was created, the spiritual beings that were embodied in their creation developed the perfect form of particular human emotions. The flower remedies are in fact tinctures of liquid healing energy, each one embodying part of the conscious life-force of the plant.

Absorbing the energy of a plant that possesses the qualities of a human emotion in its perfect, positive form counteracts the negative vibration from which the person is suffering. When someone is given a remedy which is appropriate for their condition, the plant's essence within that person helps them to regain perfect balance in the desired quality. Thus, fear is replaced by courage, anxiety by confidence, anger and resentment by love and forgiveness.

Over the past few years, a number of therapists and researchers have been discovering more and more remedies based on the energies of plants, and also on those of gems and minerals. There are now literally hundreds of remedies on the market, coming from all over the world, to deal with a huge range of emotional and spiritual imbalances.

Etheric Healing

Healing by the laying on of hands or prayer is an extremely ancient form of therapy. It comes under various names: spiritual healing, psychic healing, bioenergetic therapy, faith healing, and so on. Here it is referred to as etheric healing, since it works through and on the etheric energies of the human body. For a long time regarded with suspicion and scepticism, healing today is becoming increasingly widespread and accepted, even by some medical doctors. In the 1990s it seems that we are becoming more open to the potential of therapies that are not 'scientifically' explicable.

Healers work in a variety of ways and give a variety of explanations for how healing works. The most widespread is that the healer acts as a channel for a cosmic or spiritual energy that passes through them to the patient, stimulating the patient's own self-healing process. Some healers are aware of being helped by healing guides, some put their results down to religious faith, and some work purely with energy; nowadays many also use tools like sound, colour and crystals. This variety of beliefs and techniques does not generally affect the benefits of the healing received by patients. Successful healing seems to depend not on techniques but rather on the quality of the healer and their ability to channel the highest form of spiritual energy.

The effects of etheric healing vary from mild relaxation and pain relief to results that can only be described as miraculous. The Kahunas, according to Max Freedom Long, were able to perform extraordinary instant healings. And at Thornhill in the 1970s, I witnessed the healer Albert Best causing tumours and arthritic deposits to disappear. How do these apparently 'miraculous healings' come about?

Energy vibrates at various levels – the Kahunas referred to three levels (see Chapter 3). The most powerful healing draws on the highest and most powerful frequency – energy its highest form. The Kahunas called it Mana-Loa ('the strongest force'): healers today often refer to it as spiritual energy. It is the energy of the Higher Self.

Directed by the healer's Higher Self to the patient, it has the effect of raising the vibrational frequency of the affected part of the body until it is no longer solid. In this energy form it is healed before being rematerialised in the Physical Body. Since the Etheric Body forms a blueprint of every cell of the Physical Body, it provides a perfect template for every limb, organ and tissue. When the energy form of the dissolved area reverts to its normal solid frequency in the etheric mould, it is restored to a healthy condition.

Having witnessed the work of Albert Best at Thornhill, I can authenticate that this type of healing can and does take place. Albert was a highly gifted channel; in trance, he was taken over by two Spirit doctors in turn, who carried out operations through his hands, without opening up the Physical Body. Albert used to place his hands over the relevant area of the patient's body. The patient would feel a powerful, warm, tingling sensation, as the Spirit guide raised the vibrational frequency of the area being treated until it was no longer solid.

Albert would then withdraw from the body the energy form of the affected part, and immediately plunge his hands into a bowl of water. The water absorbed and dissipated the energy, preventing the diseased tissue from resolidifying when it returned to its normal vibrational state. He would then replace his hands on the patient, and heal the relevant area of the Etheric Body. This done, the patient could expect healing or relief from suffering. It was not uncommon for tumours to be removed in this way.

Healing of this magnitude can only be performed with the participation of the Higher Self. The Spirit guides often spoke to us through Albert during the healing. They told us that any one of us who were healers could perform similar feats, if only we had the confidence. In fact, they said that Albert did not really need their help; if he could only be convinced, he could perform this kind of healing on his own, with the help of his Higher Self.

Now, the Higher Self will never interfere in any human activity, including healing, without being asked. At Thornhill, those present often heard one or other of Albert's Spirit guides requesting the help of his Higher Self, whom he addressed as 'Father' (reminiscent of the Kahunas, who called the Higher Self 'the parental Spirit').

To contact the Higher Self the Kahunas themselves followed a specific procedure. They held that contact with the Higher Self should be initiated by the Lower or Feeling Self, who must request its participation in the healing. The reasons for this were firstly, that the Feeling Self produces the vital energy (Mana) needed by the Higher Self. Secondly, it controls all the healer's bodily functions including those involved in the healing. Thirdly, unless all three selves operate as one, complete healing cannot take place. The active participation of the Feeling Self – which constitutes 50% of our earthly being – is essential.

The Feeling Self always has to be instructed to play its full part in the healing activity, and the Kahunas achieved this through the use of ritual. The Mana, or vital energy, presented by the Feeling Self, could then be raised by the Higher Self to the highest frequency.

As we saw in Chapter 2, *The Purpose of Creation*, it was the action of consciousness upon energy that brought about the creation of the universe. Similarly, it is the consciousness of the Higher Self that causes energy to become sufficiently high in frequency to bring about changes in physical matter. And – as Long emphasises – this high-frequency energy then responds to the direction of the healer's conscious intention *almost as though it were itself conscious*.

The majority of healers ultimately derive their healing ability from their Higher Selves, whether or not they are aware of it; the exception is that when a channel like Albert Best is taken over in trance, the healing energy appears to come from the Higher Self of the Spirit doctor working through him. Most healers, however, work in a conscious state: when Spirit guides work with them, it seems that the guides draw on the energy of the healer's own Higher Self. Whether or not healers work with guides, I believe that they would all have the potential to heal as effectively as the Kahunas, if they included the Feeling Self in the process.

It is true that healers who are unaware of this concept still obtain good results. I believe this is because the majority adopt some kind of ritual before giving healing, in the form of a prayer, meditation, a breathing exercise, a request to their guides or, indeed, to their Higher Selves.

The Feeling Self is very responsive to ritual and these practices in themselves alert it to become involved with the Higher Self. However, unless the healer *consciously* invokes the participation of the Feeling Self, and instructs it to make contact with the Higher Self, the link is still tenuous and the energy less powerful than it could be. Conversely, the more aware healers are of the role of the Feeling Self, the more open they can become as channels for truly powerful healing.

At Thornhill, people came to Albert Best with a variety of complaints, including cancer: I witnessed many cases of cancer eliminated and arthritic joints restored to movement, as well as a wide range of other cures. Even so, not everyone was healed, in the sense of being cured. What was consistent was that they were relieved of physical pain and mental suffering, for truly spiritual healing affects all levels, including the emotions and the Soul-being, as well as the physical. But, as with the other forms of treatment discussed here, when an illness is serious the correction of symptoms through healing does not always lead to a permanent physical cure. We will be discussing how to achieve this in the next chapter.

❖ ❖ ❖

6. *The Cure of Illness*

❖ ❖ ❖

Of the three phases of illness – cause, correction of symptoms, and cure – the all-important third phase is often neglected. As far as the medical profession is concerned, once symptoms have been dealt with, the battle is over. But when a serious emotional and/or spiritual imbalance is involved, ill-health is sooner or later likely to return. For anyone suffering from a chronic illness, or who wants to prevent chronic illness from setting in, the first step is to understand that recurrent problems usually have an underlying cause of an emotional and possibly spiritual nature.

Once this cause has been identified and accepted, we can set about dealing with it by making the appropriate changes in lifestyle, attitudes and beliefs. This demands our active and willing participation: no matter what treatment we receive, or how effective it is in the short term, only we ourselves can bring about the state of permanent harmony that leads to real healing. This requires us to understand the role of the three selves, and – perhaps for the first time – to engage the support of the Feeling Self.

Together, the Feeling and Rational Selves form the two halves of the Ego, our total earthly self. It is the Feeling Self that not only controls the processes and wellbeing of the Physical Body; it also holds our memories and emotions, and the flawed beliefs that are so often the key to disharmony. Yet all too often the Feeling Self goes unheeded or unheard. In dealing with chronic ill-health, the Feeling Self must be convinced that the Rational Self has effectively dealt with the problem that started it in the first place: otherwise it will continue to respond as before. Therefore, for a permanent cure, there must be a joint involvement and commitment by both the Rational and the Feeling Selves.

This process of inner change does not have to be as difficult as we are sometimes led to believe. The Kahunas had some practical and extremely effective ways of embarking on this journey – and a fascinating phenomenon today is that much of the ancient wisdom known to the Kahunas is re-emerging in various ways. For example, self-help techniques like visualisation and affirmations which are encouraged by New Age therapists and self-development groups are actually methods of communicating with the Feeling Self and persuading it to change its negative beliefs.

In the field of psychology, new therapies are being developed which do not involve years of analysis, or wallowing in painful memories. In Cognitive Therapy, for instance, the psychologist helps the client to examine the truth of habitual ways of thinking and to replace negative, often irrational statements (such as, 'I am always a failure') with more positive ideas (such as recalling past successes). Neuro-Linguistic Programming (NLP) is another method of rapidly changing attitudes, which often engages the Feeling Self very directly through bodily sensations and actions. Other new, forward-looking therapies are emerging all the time, based on changing negative beliefs and attitudes.

While it can be helpful to seek the support of a counsellor or self-development group, this is not always essential. The key to good health – emotional as well as physical – lies in establishing a new relationship with the Feeling Self.

Identifying the Cause of Disharmony

People are often aware, or partly aware, of the emotional problems underlying their chronic ailments, but are unwilling or simply unsure how to deal with them. Others know that something is not working in their lives, but do not necessarily relate it to their state of health. Not everyone wants to: life would obviously be much easier if health could be restored simply by taking pills or undergoing surgery, without the need for self-examination. Unfortunately, this rarely happens.

The Kahunas spoke of the barriers to healing as 'something eating inside', which they often identified as guilt. These barriers also include factors like fear of failure (or of success), anxiety, unexpressed grief, suppressed anger, or feelings of general unworthiness and inadequacy.

Such emotions can affect people's health in various ways, *some of which* have a very clear connection with their physical symptoms. For example, fear of failure can lead to stomach upsets before exams or interviews. The sense of being overburdened can produce shoulder problems or backache. A sore throat may result from failing or fearing to express oneself. In fact, one clue to the cause of an illness is to ask yourself, 'What does this prevent me from doing?' Sometimes the links are less obvious, perhaps because the memory of a painful experience has been suppressed. Patients who visit natural therapists – particularly those who practise counselling, or who are strongly intuitive – may find the cause emerging through discussion during their therapy.

In fact, there is a part of you which knows very well why you are ill – the Feeling Self. And you may find that it is very willing to tell you, if you ask it. Simply go into a relaxed, meditative state; then tell your Feeling Self that you would like its help, and ask it what you need to know. The answer will come in the form of a mental message: it may come in words, images, or a feeling. If you do not get an immediate answer, it may well come a little later in the form of a dream.

It is also by working with the Feeling Self that you can eradicate the cause. Before describing how to do this, however, it may be useful to review the roles and qualities of the three Selves.

The Role of the Three Selves

The Subconscious, Rational and Higher Selves are three separate parts of us, each of which has an individual and necessary role: the more they can work together, the healthier and more effective we can become.

The Feeling Self is close to though not quite synonymous with, the subconscious mind. It controls our involuntary bodily systems, and holds our memories and emotions. These three are strongly linked (emotional memories are stored not only in the Etheric Body, but also in the cells and muscles of the Physical Body), and it is with these that we find the key to 'the thing eating inside'.

As we saw in Chapter 4, the cause of illness very often lies with the flawed beliefs and attitudes instilled into the Feeling Self in childhood. These may conflict with ideas which the Rational Self acquires later in life – particularly as the Feeling Self makes no distinction between past, present and future. When the conflict is strong enough, the

Feeling Self will react with physical symptoms, or highly charged emotional responses.

The Feeling Self occupies the centre of the body – the area corresponding to the solar plexus chakra, which governs self-esteem, and feelings of fear or courage.

A misunderstanding of psychology commonly leads people to believe that the Feeling Self is something to be feared. This is far from the case. It is much more like a child which has the capacity for all the positive emotions, as well as the less positive ones. It is, as Long puts it, 'dear and bright and loving... endlessly faithful and willing and eager.' It corresponds very closely to what New Age therapists call the 'Inner Child'. It has the capacity to be joyful, creative and intuitive and, with the help of the Rational Self, it can become our ally.

The Rational Self, or Conscious Self, is logical and unemotional. Its role is to act as parent, guide and teacher to the Feeling Self. Unfortunately, unless we are aware of this concept, it is only too easy either to suppress the Feeling Self or to let it run the show – in the form of over-emotional reactions, for instance, or by continuing to hold negative beliefs about oneself and life in general. It may stop us from doing something the Rational Self has agreed to do – such as giving up addictions and making other changes in lifestyle. When we start consciously communicating with the Feeling Self, however, the Rational Self can begin to take charge of the situation, and change it.

The Higher Self is our connection with the spiritual realm. It is in turn parent and guide to the two other selves, and like a good parent it will only intervene if we ask it to. It is reached through meditation and during our periods of deepest sleep, and the most powerful form of contact with it is made via the Feeling, or Lower Self (see Chapter 7). It is vitally important, therefore, that we begin to communicate with the Feeling Self.

Befriending the Feeling Self

To begin a dialogue with the Feeling Self, choose a time when you will not be disturbed, and sit down quietly. Allow yourself to enter a relaxed, meditative state, and invite your Feeling Self to make itself known. You can do this silently, but it will probably be more effective to speak out loud. It can help if you imagine the Feeling Self sitting in a chair opposite you.

The Feeling Self may reply in the form of words, mental pictures, or feelings. It may even want to write or draw its answers, so have a pen and some paper handy. You can experiment with your method of communication: regard it as a game, rather than a serious test – the Feeling Self enjoys games.

If you do not get a strong response on the first occasion, don't lose patience: if it has never been truly listened to before, the Feeling Self may be hesitant at first – particularly if it has come in for a lot of criticism in the past. You may need to repeat the process more than once before you can communicate fully.

The Feeling Self may need reassuring that you are on its side and want its wellbeing. If, as a child, you did not receive all the love you wanted, the Feeling Self will still be carrying that sense of being unloved. Now is the time when your Rational Self can give it the love and approval it needs. We are often told that it is important to love ourselves, and this becomes much easier if you imagine that unloved self as a little child, eager to be appreciated and to cooperate in this new game.

It is easier to communicate with the Feeling Self if you give it a name – which need not be the same as yours. Ask it what it would like to be called, and listen to what comes into your mind. Then, in future, always address it by name. Max Freedom Long called his 'George'; he began his own communication with 'George' by asking it for pleasant childhood memories, and was flooded by warm memories to which he had given little thought over the years.

Through communicating with the Feeling Self, you can learn a great deal about it, and its beliefs – as well as the cause of any physical problems you are suffering from. This may stem from beliefs that the Rational Self is already aware of, but has not managed to change – or you may be surprised by something completely new. The next step is to find ways of persuading the Feeling Self to change the beliefs that are impairing the healing process.

Guilt and Forgiveness

For the Kahunas, the 'thing eating inside', which activated most problems and prevented a full cure, was a sense of sin or guilt; they held that if the Feeling Self believed a person had 'sinned' and deserved punishment, it would punish them through illness or accidents. Healing could only take effect if the Feeling Self believed it deserved to be healed. It was therefore important to clear any guilt feelings, however minor, for full healing to take place.

Many people harbour underlying guilt feelings. Few of us go through life without doing a few things of which we feel ashamed. This can be worsened by a strictly religious upbringing (which can leave rational adults with a sense of sin about enjoying all kinds of pleasures), by a childhood in which normal childish activities were labelled 'naughty' or 'wicked', or by parents who told us we caused them pain or disappointment when we did not follow their chosen path for us.

The Kahunas themselves taught that the only sin was to hurt another person – to which we might add 'or any living being'. They summed this up neatly in the phrase, 'No hurt, no sin.' While they recognised the existence of Higher Beings, they also saw that by their very nature, there was nothing a human being could do that would hurt such beings. This is very important: if you believe in a God of love and forgiveness who is a perfect spiritual being, that spiritual being *cannot* be hurt by our activities. Nor is a perfect Spirit likely to indulge in the very human emotion of anger. What can happen, if we behave badly enough, is that we become cut off from our Higher Selves. This may sadden the Higher Self, it will not hurt it. The loss of contact will, however, diminish our own lives.

Looking rationally at the cause of your guilt, your Rational Self may see that it is in fact quite undeserved. But it is the Feeling Self which needs to be convinced. The Kahunas dealt with this by performing specific rituals, which included fasting, purification (through washing or bathing), and giving away money or goods. These very physical activities helped to convince the Feeling Self that the sin was expiated and forgiven.

You may like to try carrying out such a ritual for yourself. Fasting could take the form of a complete fast, or of giving up something you like for a day or two. Take a bath specifically for the purpose of washing away past sins or guilts. If you have hurt someone in the past, you could write them a letter of apology – it is not necessary to send it unless this is appropriate. Finally, give some money to charity, over and above what you normally give, or perform some other generous action. You can then, as Rational Self, reassure the Feeling Self that it has been forgiven.

Re-examining Your Beliefs

A problem which is possibly even more common than guilt – though closely allied to it – is low self-esteem. In our communications with the Feeling Self, therefore, it will respond to praise and encouragement.

Even well-meaning parents may feel it right to focus more on criticism than praise, instilling into children the feeling that they are not quite good enough. As a result many people carry into adult life a view of themselves that does not tally with reality, and which affects their general potential as well as their health. (We should not forget, of course, that the converse may also be true: it is possible to grow up with an over-inflated idea of one's talents and self-importance. This can also lead to inner and outer conflict in adult life!)

In adulthood, the Rational Self may form new opinions about its self-worth, or may *want* to form them but is obstructed by the Feeling Self. It may not even be aware that the Feeling Self's beliefs are erroneous, formed as they were in childhood when the Rational Self was not yet able to judge their validity. Faulty childhood beliefs are sometimes held with absolute conviction by otherwise intelligent, rational people: over-judgmental parents, for instance, were probably themselves brought up to believe unquestioningly that children benefit from constant criticism.

Some beliefs appear rational because they are held by society at large. For example, many people unthinkingly accept society's view that the way to happiness is found through achieving material success, despite evidence to the contrary. Beliefs about racial or religious superiority or inferiority may be held without question – until a whole nation is forced to reconsider them, as with South Africa. Such beliefs may appear to be consciously formed, but are in fact strongly held by the Feeling Self, which is why it can require a major upheaval to change them. A classic case is that of Northern Ireland, where intelligent people have found it almost impossible to shift their stance, having been brought up from infancy to hold fixed attitudes about people whose beliefs differ from their own.

You can tell if a belief is also held by the Feeling Self if contradicting it evokes an emotional response; such beliefs may need some recon-sideration. Changing flawed beliefs will benefit not only your health, but your future activities and relationships.

Changing your Beliefs

Having understood and accepted the cause of your health problems, the next stage in the healing process is to convince the Feeling Self that the beliefs that triggered them can be changed. As you communicate with the Feeling Self, you will make a good start simply by gaining new insights into the truth of its beliefs; the Feeling Self is often will-ing to change illogical beliefs once the Rational Self shows that they *are* illogical.

Remember that thought-forms are bundles of living energy; as you change your beliefs, you can replace unwanted, unrealistic thought-forms by positive, more realistic ones. Focusing on these, and acting on them, will give them the energy to grow in strength so that they can eventually materialise in reality.

You can back up this process in a number of ways. Bear in mind that the Feeling Self is very responsive to repetition and habit. It also responds to physical stimuli, which include speech, the written word, images, and physical actions. One method of helping it to absorb your new beliefs is the use of affirmations, positive statements about oneself, which should be written, or spoken, in the present tense: for example, 'Every day in every way I am getting better and better.' They should be repeated a number of times. The act of speaking or writing helps to get the message through to the Feeling Self by giving it a physical role in the process.

There is one caution here. You may find your Feeling Self having a strong negative reaction to some affirmations. Repeating, 'I am a confident person' will change nothing if your Feeling Self repeatedly responds, 'But I'm not!' So take note of any responses like this, together with your physical reactions, and talk with your Feeling Self about the source of its belief and how it could be changed. For instance, you could write a description of the way you want to be, or draw a picture of yourself in the situation you want, and put it up where your Feeling Self can see it. This will help your Feeling Self to understand that change is possible.

Visualisation is another tool which you can use to picture yourself in a perfect state of health. Presented with this positive image, the Feeling Self takes it as reality, which encourages it to make the necessary bodily changes to bring it about. While visualising, the more relaxed you are the more effective this will be. Don't worry if you can't 'see' very clearly at first, and make use of your senses of feeling and hearing as your visual imagination. You can also use visualisation to picture yourself acting in new ways, such as behaving confidently at a job interview, or remaining calm in a situation which would normally upset you.

Affirmations and visualisation are both ways of creating new thought-forms: they are all the more effective if you can consciously engage the Feeling Self in the activity. The more you practise them, the stronger the new, positive thought-forms will be.

Make it a point, too, to *act* on the beliefs that you want your Feeling Self to hold. If you want it to feel valued, behave in a way that shows you value it: this might involve making changes to your life-style, like adopting a more balanced diet, or taking regular exercise. If you want to deal with an addiction, explain to the Feeling Self why you need to give up smoking or chocolate. Then keep to your decision, so that the Feeling Self understands that you mean business. You can also, of course, reward it with praise or by doing something you and it enjoy.

A highly effective physical means of impressing the Feeling Self is to clear up your environment; getting rid of unwanted rubbish from cupboards or shelves demonstrates to it that you are also clearing out out-dated beliefs and ideas. If you have a garden, make use of the act of weeding by doing it with the consciousness that you are 'weeding out' unwanted negative thoughts.

To help the Feeling Self absorb the new ideas you want it to hold, make it a habit to read books that support your new way of thinking (some are listed at the back of this book). It can be very helpful to join a self-development class or group, where you will get the support of other people on a similar path. For example, if self-esteem is a basic problem, assertiveness training classes not only encourage you to examine your beliefs about yourself, but enable you to literally act out new ways of being and reacting.

You can also support the changes you want to make by taking flower remedies, taking up appropriate, energy-oriented exercise (like Yoga, T'ai Chi or Qi Gung), and listening to great music. Try to cultivate a positive outlook on life, not by denying what is wrong but by seeking the good in the people and events around you.

The Feeling Self and the Emotions

When you embark on this process of self-exploration, you are likely to come across negative feelings such as fear, or anger, or unexpressed grief. All emotions come from the Feeling Self, and they need to be paid attention to.

Whatever emotions are causing problems, remember that *the emotions are the province of the Feeling Self alone.* This can help the Rational Self to regard emotions dispassionately, without being overwhelmed by them or attempting to suppress them. Nor is it necessary to wallow in them: the Rational Self can help the Feeling Self to overcome bad memories by giving it new, constructive lines to work on, in the form of new beliefs and activities. But painful emotions do need to be acknowledged if they are to be healed.

If the Feeling Self is fearful, the Rational Self must patiently allow it to express its fears – which may well include the fear of change – and reassure it that there is no longer any need for fear. In the case of anger, speaking your anger aloud (not necessarily to the person who caused it) helps to move the energy that has been holding it in. If the Feeling Self is full of grief, it may be that as a child you were not allowed to shed the tears you needed to. The Rational Self, as a kind parent, must allow the Feeling Self to express that grief.

If you find yourself getting into painful emotions, don't stay with them for too long: give yourself a time limit, and always end such sessions with some positive statements and actions. Energetic physical activity like walking, running and dancing, also help to release the physical effects produced by deep emotions, while flower remedies can help to heal them. Some people may need the support of a counsellor or therapist: no-one should be afraid of seeking professional help at times of emotional crisis.

When Cure is Slow

The methods outlined above, if taken seriously and practised regularly, can not only affect the course of chronic illness but can improve life all round. Do not expect results to be instant, particularly when a condition has been present for some time; ideally these techniques could be used to prevent ill-health from setting in in the first place. If an illness has taken some time to build up, it can also take time to cure, and there may be some conditions which cannot be cured completely if a great deal of physical deterioration has already occurred.

There may be also cases, as we saw in Chapter 4, when there are spiritual reasons for a person unconsciously choosing to experience the discomforts of a disabling or terminal illness, or even a premature death. They may be part of the lifeplan chosen by the Soul in order to further one's spiritual development by undergoing particular experiences. They also often serve the evolution of those around, giving them the opportunity to grow through experiencing a caring role.

Even if you do not achieve a full recovery, establishing a new, creative collaboration with your

Feeling Self can only benefit your life and your relationships; it will help you not only to understand why you have become ill, but to come to terms with the problem. And, whether you are ill or not, your life will be greatly enhanced if you also use the Feeling Self to build stronger links with your Higher Self, and to align yourself more closely with your true purpose.

7. Living in Harmony with the Higher Self

❖ ❖ ❖

When you begin a regular dialogue with the Feeling Self, you will probably find aspects of your life changing, or demanding to be changed. Try to pace these changes; when you are learning any kind of new skill, periods of focussed learning need to be followed by periods of assimilation.

As a result of your new relationship with yourself, you may be making new discoveries about your self-worth, your values, and your potential. You may discover that you and your Feeling Self need to express more creativity, or you may decide to develop other gifts that have been lying latent. You should also find that any self-imposed limitations begin to lift, as you give yourself permission to live more fully. All of these will feed into your working life and your relationships with others, and set you on the path for a fruitful future life, as well as a healthier one.

When we look at old people, it is possible to recognise those who have developed a good relationship with their Feeling Self, and those who have not. In old age, some people revert to childish patterns of behaviour and can become decidedly cantankerous, selfish and unreasonable, as the control exercised by the Rational Self weakens. It is true that some people often find themselves obliged to be dependent upon others, and they may resent this. If they have not understood the role of their Feeling Self, it is liable to express its resentment in a childish way, not understanding that there is a spiritual purpose behind this loss of independence.

There are two important learning periods in our lives, one in childhood, and one in old age. Losing one's independence in old age provides a final opportunity for self-development by experiencing a different relationship with those around – by learning to receive care instead, perhaps, of always being in the role of provider and controller. If we can learn, at any age, to live in greater harmony with ourselves, our relationships with others can only benefit both in the short-term and for the remainder of our lives. Life then becomes a continuing journey of growth towards greater wisdom, rather than an inevitable deterioration.

As we saw in Chapter 2, the purpose of human existence is for us, as spiritual beings, to experience life in a material environment, so that we can ultimately return to the spiritual realm to which our Souls belong. You can be greatly helped in this by making contact with the Higher Self, the spiritual part of you that is watching over your progress and longs to give help and guidance, if only you will let it.

Contacting the Higher Self

In New Age circles today, people are encouraged to make contact with their Higher Selves, and many in fact achieve this. However, there is a risk of seeking enlightenment through the Higher Self alone, while by-passing the Feeling Self. This not only makes the contact less powerful than it might be: it could be the reason why some apparently very spiritual people nonetheless have problems with their relationships and day-to-day living. As outlined in Chapter 2, we are subject to two forces: the upward, spiritual force, and the downward, material force. If only one predominates, we are thrown out of balance. It is important to remember that our object is to experience ourselves as spiritual beings *within a physical body and a material environment*. And the Feeling Self is, of course, the controller of the Physical Body.

The desire to go straight to the Higher Self is partly the result of the Western religious tradition, with its belief – still held in some quarters – that the body and its natural feelings are sinful, and must be denied or 'overcome'. In Eastern traditions the role of the body has been better understood, and many Eastern forms of meditation engage the Feeling Self through the body by means of physical exercises – Yoga in India and T'ai Chi in China, for instance. In their healing activities, the Kahunas made a point of building up vital force (Mana) before offering it to the Higher Self to be raised to its highest form. Yoga and T'ai Chi are both methods of building up energy, so are deep relaxation, breathing exercises, and some forms of dance. And since they all involve the body, they are all ways of encouraging the participation of the Feeling Self. So even if you do not practise a specific technique, it can be helpful to do some physical stretching and deep breathing before contacting the Higher Self.

Choose a quiet time and place for this. Remember that the Feeling Self likes symbols and physical acts: lighting a candle or placing a favourite crystal in front of you will alert it to the fact that you are engaging in something special. If you practise this regularly, remember that the Feeling Self is a creature of habit, and if possible choose a regular time, place, and symbolic act to alert it to your intentions.

Sit with your spine straight (but not rigid) and your feet flat on the floor, and close your eyes. Now, become aware of your breathing, and allow it to become slower and deeper (deep breathing should not be forced). This will help you to quieten the mind to achieve a meditational state.

Next, first make your need known to the Feeling Self: tell it that you would like guidance from your Higher Self. If you have a specific question or problem, now is the time to pose it. Then sit quietly with your eyes closed, and allow the Higher Self its space in your mind.

Do not expect anything dramatic to occur; you may only be conscious of your mind becoming calmer. Some people experience a feeling of love and security. Sometimes the answer to a problem simply drops into the mind in the form of words, a mental image, or just a sense of knowing. Quite often the answers you seek will come less directly, and not necessarily at the time of asking. You might find yourself being led to a particular book, or an unexpected meeting or conversation may provide you with new information or a new insight. With regular practice you will also find that as you go about the day your intuition will be sharper, and you will have a clearer sense of direction.

Sleep and Dreams

We are all in touch with our Higher Selves during our deepest periods of sleep. These are the times when the Ego and the Astral Body together leave the Physical Body to be renewed and re-balanced in the realm of Spirit. As a rule we have no conscious recollection of these journeys, though most people will have some inkling of them at times – it is quite common, for example, to wake up knowing the solution to a problem. This can be encouraged by asking your Astral Body before you go to sleep to seek the answer to any question that is bothering you. The first time I tried this myself, immediately on waking I found myself going to a particular book; it opened at a page which included the answer to that question. This is a natural human faculty which everyone could use to advantage.

It is also very common to receive guidance through dreams, so it is worth paying them some attention. Not all dreams have significance, of course; many are simply a way of clearing the brain of the mental business of the day. Dreams that have important meanings for us tend to be the ones that wake us up, or leave us with a deep and lasting impression. Recurring dreams are always important; they indicate that we need to pay attention to something we may be trying to ignore.

Keeping a dream diary encourages the process of communication; if you start writing your dreams down in a note-book they will become progressively easier to remember. Keep a pen and paper by your bed, so that you can note them down as soon as possible after waking, before the details fade away. Some people prefer to keep a tape-recorder at the bedside, which enables them to record any dreams during the night without having to put the light on. When you come to write the dream out next day, you may be surprised to realise its meaning.

Learning the language of your dreams can take a little practice. Though they come from the Higher Self, they are always mediated by the Feeling Self, which tends to pass the information on to us in symbolic form, or through puns or word-play. For instance, dreaming you have something in your eye may signify that there is something your 'I' is not seeing clearly. So pay attention to any elements in your dreams that do not have an immediately obvious meaning, and ask yourself what they might symbolise.

It is also worth explicitly asking for helpful dreams before you go to sleep. Remember that the Higher Self *wants* the opportunity to help and guide you.

Planning Your Life

It can be useful to take time now and again to think about what you really want to happen in your life. While the Feeling Self deals with past memories, it is the Higher Self that helps us to form the future, using the thought-forms created by the plans and desires of the two lower selves. The clearer and more decisive you are about what you want and where you want to go, the clearer the thought-forms which go to construct your future. The reason people so often do not get what they want is that the thought-forms of what they desire are mixed up with the fears and doubts of the Feeling Self.

Ultimately, what happens in our lives is a result of the thought-forms, and clusters of thought-forms, created by both the Rational and the Feeling Selves. Thought-forms have an energy and power of their own, which materialise in real events. Albert Best's

Spirit guides used to tell us, 'Thoughts are real and living things, so you should be extremely careful about what you think. They often cause a lot of problems.'

Everything that you think is potentially capable of being materialised. This is why some people suffer from 'self-fulfilling prophecies': the person who says, 'I never have any luck' is literally building for themselves a luckless future. On the other hand, re-programming the ideas of the Feeling Self, as described in Chapter 6, depletes the energy of negative thought-forms; focusing on new, positive beliefs will create new thought-forms, while repetition will energise them. Ultimately that energy will create the new reality you want to bring about.

Planning is best done by the Rational Self, but you can engage the help of the Feeling Self by letting it know that you are allowed to have what you want (providing it hurts no-one else). Make sure that you have its full participation. For example, the Rational Self may decide quite logically that you need a larger income. If the Feeling Self has at some stage been taught that the desire for money is greedy or even sinful, it will need to be convinced otherwise so that it does not sabotage your efforts.

You can also help the Feeling Self to cooperate by taking some active or symbolic step towards getting what you want. For example, if you want a new home, buy an object or a piece of furniture that you intend to put in it. Affirmations and visualisation are also useful: the Kahunas would pray aloud for what they needed, and repeat the prayer three times, to ensure that the Feeling Self carried the thought-form to the Higher Self.

Your Higher Self and Other People

You can use your contact with your Higher Self to improve your relationships with other people, and to help others if you wish, through prayer or medi-tation. Incidentally, if you already use prayer in your life, do not be concerned about the idea of praying to the Higher Self: as mentioned earlier, the Kahunas believed in the existence of higher beings, and regarded the Higher Self as the intermediary in contacting those higher beings. Similarly, all our prayers, whoever they are directed to, reach their destination through the mediation of the Higher Self.

If you are having difficulty with a particular person, it may help to remember that *everyone* has a Higher Self: that we are *all* spiritual beings and that at a much higher level, we are all part of the same whole. There is a level at which all Higher Selves are linked: this is one reason why group meditations and prayers can be so powerful.

You can help to resolve a problem with some-one else by engaging both the Feeling Self and the Higher Self, either in meditation or before going to sleep. If, for instance, someone has upset you, remember that the emotional upset is the response of the Feeling Self, which may be reacting like a hurt child. You can help to get rid of the upset both by recognising this, and by explaining the situation to your Feeling Self. It is quite likely that the other person's Feeling Self is also behaving childishly! Then ask your Higher Self to contact the Higher Self of the other person, and to help to harmonise the relations between you. Then, stop thinking about the problem – brooding over it will only perpetuate it by continuing to energise negative thought-forms. Dealt with in this way, solutions to interpersonal problems often come about in unexpected ways: you may wake up seeing things quite differently, or receive a different reaction from the other person next time you meet, or they may simply move out of your orbit.

In Chapter 6 we described the importance of forgiving yourself, to free yourself of real or imaginary guilt. Forgiving others is another important way of clearing negativity from your system. It is not always easy to do, for if someone has treated you badly the Feeling Self may continue to feel hurt for a long time. Since it has no sense of past or future, it can go on holding that sense of hurt in the present unless the Rational Self takes action to change it.

Forgiving others does not mean that you condone or approve of their behaviour: rather, it is a way of releasing the effects of their behaviour from your system. In fact, the person who benefits most will be yourself, since emotions like anger and resentment deplete energy, and are definitely harmful to long-term health. So, explain to your Feeling Self why you need to let go of that past experience. It can be helpful to visualise the other person sitting opposite you. Be aware that they, too, have a Higher Self; then, tell them how their behaviour made you feel, and imagine them telling you they are sorry for their actions. This may be what the Feeling Self needs to hear in order finally to forgive them and let go of the hurt.

You can also ask for the help of the Higher Self in healing or praying for others. When you pray for another person, or send them healing thoughts, your thoughts will automatically go to the other person's Higher Self as well, maximising the healing energy available to them.

Going Further

I have tried to share with you here what I have found to be a rational explanation as to the causes and cures of ill-health, and my own understanding of the importance of the spiritual dimension in health – one that tends to be overlooked or not properly understood. It is offered for readers to take as a possible model of healing, which they can explore further if they wish. Following the methods outlined here will help you to heal the conflict between the over-all needs of your Soul and the needs of the Ego – including the body, mind and emotions – in the material world. For those who want to explore them more deeply, a number of books are recommended for further reading on page 98.

Further Reading

Edward Bach, *The Twelve Healers and Other Remedies*, The C W Daniel Company Ltd, 1933

Edward Bach, *Heal Thyself, An Explanation of the Real Cause and Cure of Disease*, The C W Daniel Company, 1931

Gill Edwards, *Stepping Into the Magic, A New Approach to Everyday Life*, Piatkus, 1993

Homoeopathy, The Family Handbook, Thorsons, 1992

Serge Kahili King, PhD, *Mastering Your Hidden Self, A Guide to the Huna Way*, The Theosophical Publishing House, 1985

Serge Kahili King, PhD, *Urban Shaman, A Handbook for Personal and Planetary Transformation*, Simon & Schuster, 1990

Dr Andrew Lockie, *The Family Guide to Homoeopathy*, Elm Tree Books 1989; (paperback) Hamish Hamilton, 1990

Max Freedom Long, *The Secret Science Behind*

Miracles, DeVorss Publications, 1948, 1976

Max Freedom Long, *The Secret Science At Work*, DeVorss & Company, 1953, 1988

Dennis Milner and Edward Smart, *The Loom of Creation*, Neville Spearman, 1975

Dennis Milner (ed.), *Explorations of Consciousness*, Neville Spearman, 1978

Mechthild Scheffer, *Bach Flower Therapy, Theory and Practice*, Thorsons 1986

Mechthild Scheffer, *Keys to the Soul*, The C W Daniel Company, 1997

Steiner, Rudolf, *Theosophy*, Anthroposophic Press, 1922

Steiner, Rudolf, *The Occult Science – An Outline*, Rudolf Steiner Press, 1909

Nora Weeks, *The Medical Discoveries of Edward Bach, Physician*, The C W Daniel Company Ltd, 1973

Index